Hearing the Call

Read the text messages.
Fill in your text responses in the phones at the bottom of the page.

At Home

This lesson aims to develop the children's understanding of what the prophetic call means by pointing to examples of it.

Pray together:

May the Lord put his words in my mouth,
may his Spirit lift me up,
may I be filled with his love. Amen.

Jeremiah Hears the Call

Ever wondered what you and your friends think is really important?
Well look no further! Do our fab quiz and find out.

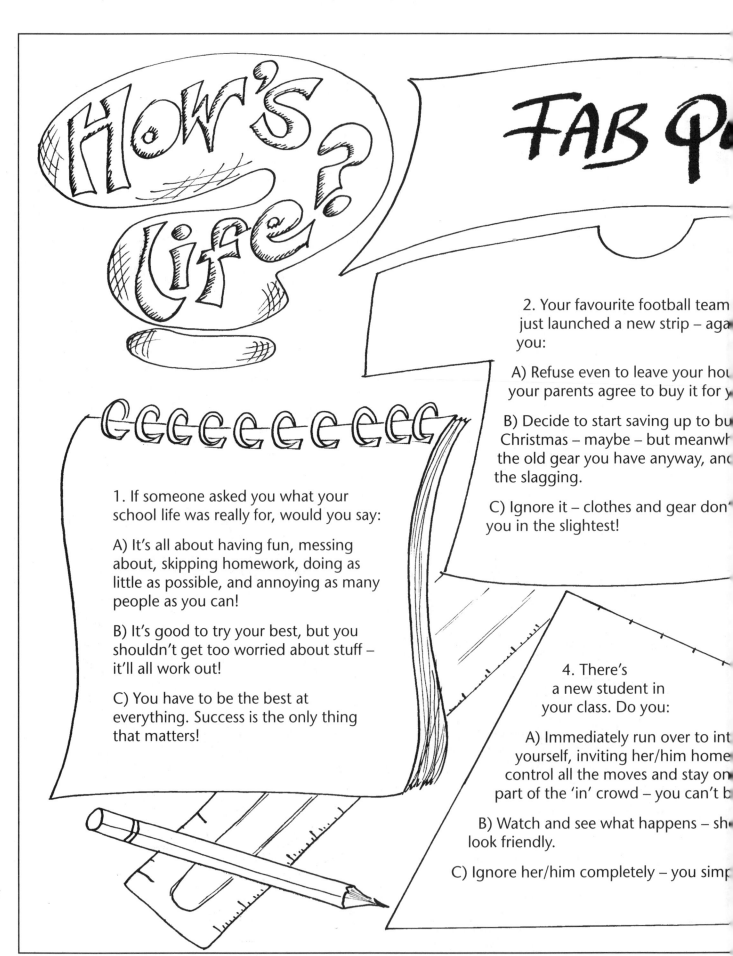

How's Life?

FAB Q...

1. If someone asked you what your school life was really for, would you say:

A) It's all about having fun, messing about, skipping homework, doing as little as possible, and annoying as many people as you can!

B) It's good to try your best, but you shouldn't get too worried about stuff – it'll all work out!

C) You have to be the best at everything. Success is the only thing that matters!

2. Your favourite football team just launched a new strip – aga you:

A) Refuse even to leave your hou your parents agree to buy it for y

B) Decide to start saving up to bu Christmas – maybe – but meanwh the old gear you have anyway, and the slagging.

C) Ignore it – clothes and gear don' you in the slightest!

4. There's a new student in your class. Do you:

A) Immediately run over to int yourself, inviting her/him home control all the moves and stay on part of the 'in' crowd – you can't b

B) Watch and see what happens – sh look friendly.

C) Ignore her/him completely – you simp

Pray together:
Father in heaven, you love me, you're with me night and day.
I want to love you always in all I do and say.
I'll try to please you, Father. Bless me through the day. Amen.

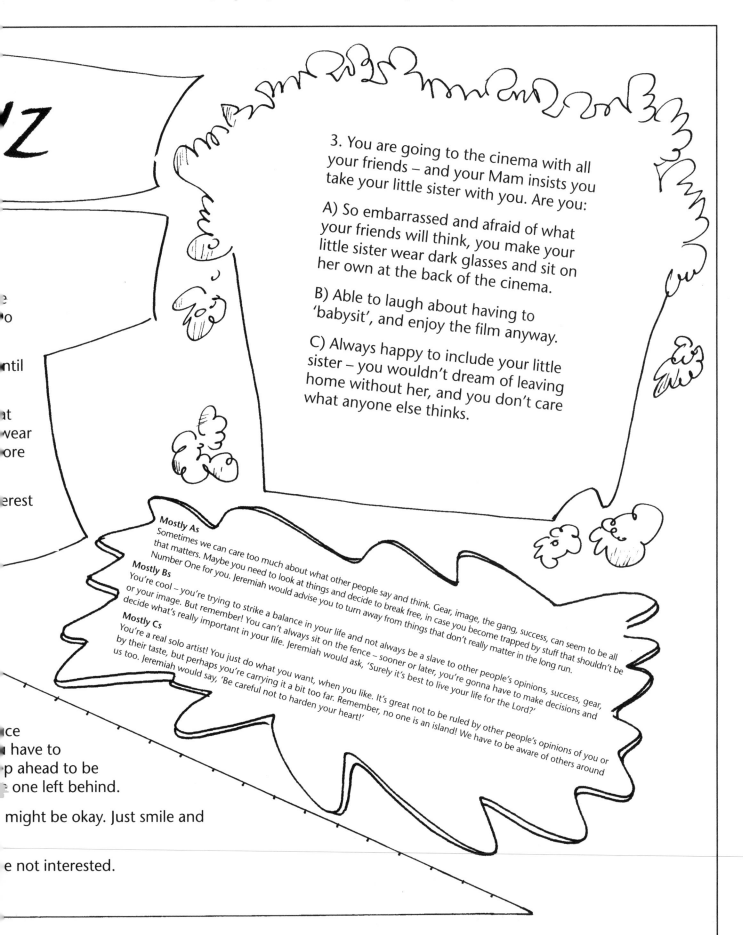

3. You are going to the cinema with all your friends – and your Mam insists you take your little sister with you. Are you:

A) So embarrassed and afraid of what your friends will think, you make your little sister wear dark glasses and sit on her own at the back of the cinema.

B) Able to laugh about having to 'babysit', and enjoy the film anyway.

C) Always happy to include your little sister – you wouldn't dream of leaving home without her, and you don't care what anyone else thinks.

Mostly As
Sometimes we can care too much about what other people say and think. Gear, image, the gang, success, can seem to be all that matters. Maybe you need to look at things and decide to break free, in case you become trapped by stuff that shouldn't be Number One for you. Jeremiah would advise you to turn away from things that don't really matter in the long run.

Mostly Bs
You're cool – you're trying to strike a balance in your life and not always be a slave to other people's opinions, success, gear, or your image. But remember! You can't always sit on the fence – sooner or later, you're gonna have to make decisions and decide what's really important in your life. Jeremiah would ask, 'Surely it's best to live your life for the Lord?'

Mostly Cs
You're a real solo artist! You just do what you want, when you like. It's great not to be ruled by other people's opinions of you or by their taste, but perhaps you're carrying it a bit too far. Remember, no one is an island! We have to be aware of others around us too. Jeremiah would say, 'Be careful not to harden your heart!'

Jesus and Prophecy

Using the letters supplied, write in Hebrew 'The Spirit of the Lord is upon me'. (As it is Hebrew, start at the top right-hand corner, and work from right to left.)

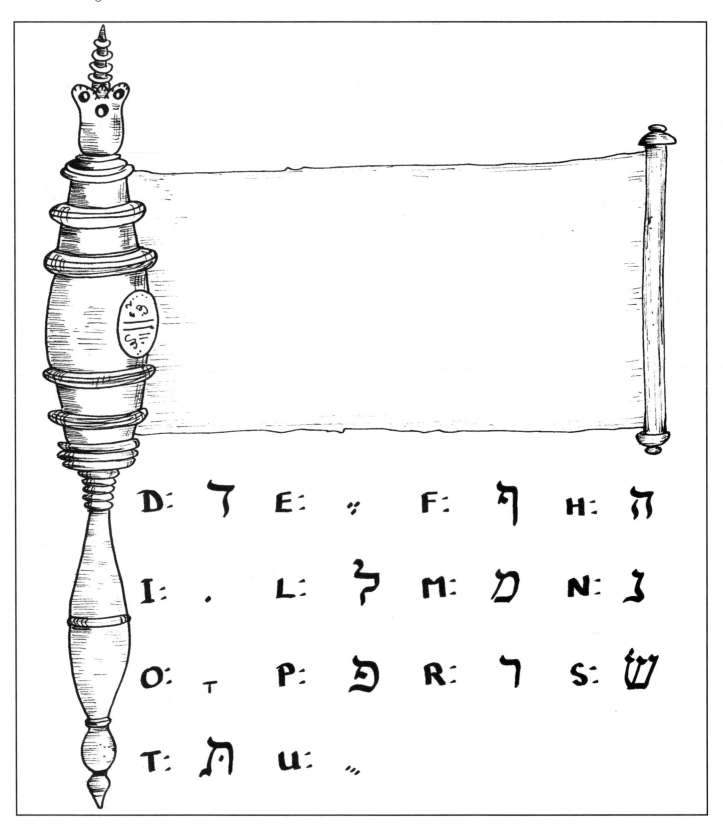

At Home

This lesson aims to show that what was foretold by the prophets of old is fulfilled and surpassed in the teachings and actions of Jesus.

Pray together:

Holy Spirit, I want to do what is right. Help me.
Holy Spirit, I want to live like Jesus. Guide me.
Holy Spirit, I want to pray like Jesus. Teach me. Amen.

The Spirit of Prophecy

Draw a picture of one of today's prophets and write an article on 'prophecy today'.

ALIVE-O TIMES
fmm.   *Sm u mm 2om.*   *www. mm .com.*

TODAY'S PROPHET

At Home   In this lesson we revisit the children's experience of prophecy in their own lives and in the modern world.

Pray together:

Christ be with me. Christ be beside me.
Christ be before me. Christ be behind me.
Christ at my right hand. Christ at my left hand.
Christ be with me everywhere I go.
Christ be my friend, forever and ever. Amen.

Mary and the Mysteries of Light

If you were inventing five new mysteries of the Rosary, what ones would you choose? Write the titles and draw the pictures of your new mysteries.

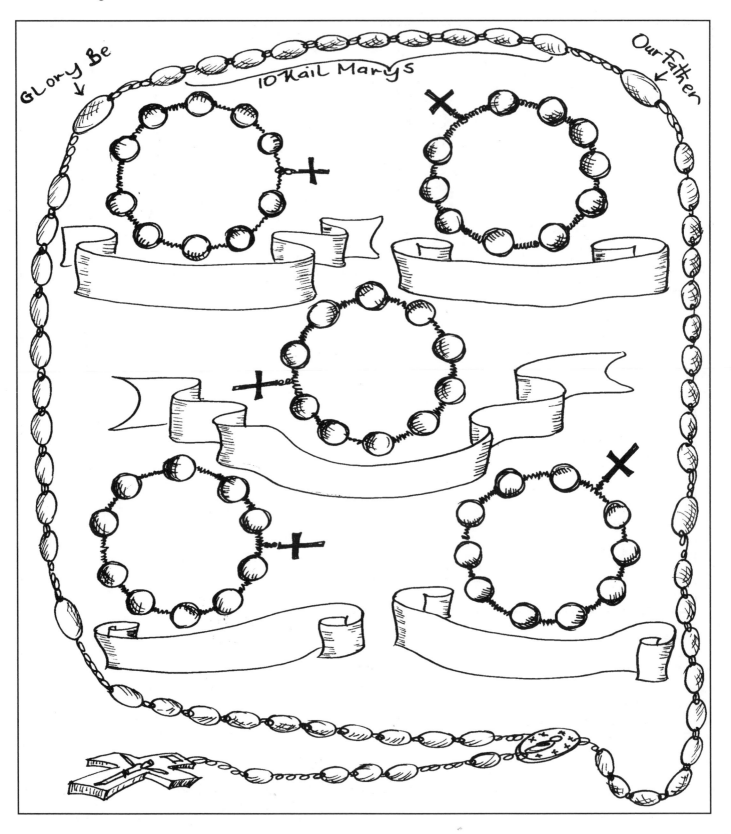

At Home

In this lesson we help to deepen the children's appreciation of Mary. We introduce them to the 'Mysteries of Light' of the Rosary.

Pray together:

Pray for us, O holy Mother of God,
that we may be made worthy of the promises of Christ. Amen.

The Saints

Draw an icon of your favourite saint.

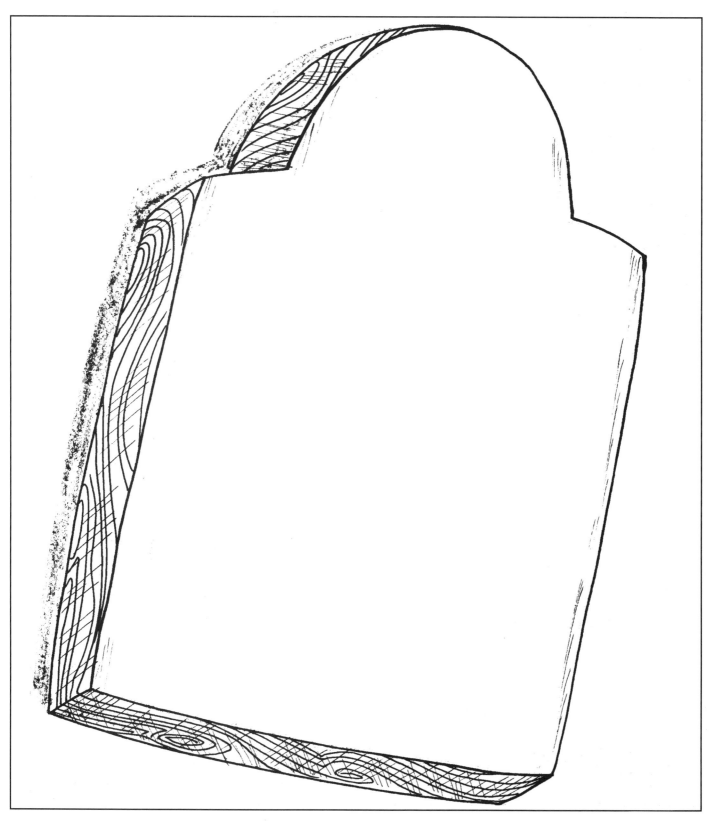

At Home

In earlier years the children have heard of Saints Patrick, Brigid, Columba, Gobnait, Brendan and Canaire. This year we introduce them to two more Irish saints – St Kevin and St Lawrence O'Toole. We also introduce them to icons.

Pray together:

Glóir don Athair, agus don Mhac, agus don Spiorad Naomh.
Mar a bhí ó thús, mar atá anois, mar a bheas go brách, le saol na saol. Áiméan.

The Garden Story

List good and bad experiences on the lines provided below.
A start has been made for you.

At Home   This lesson introduces the children to the story of the fall of Adam and Eve.

Pray together:

O my God, help me to remember the times
when I didn't live as Jesus asked me to.
Help me to be sorry and to try again. Amen.

ALIVE-O 7

Commandments 1

Try this quiz and learn how the commandments can free you to love God and others!

How do you, see yourself?

1. MONEY! FUN! MUSIC! SPORT! CLOTHES! THINGS! GOD! POWER! TV! If you were to arrange these in order of importance from 1 to 9, where would you (honestly and confidentially) place your relationship with God?
   a) In the top three of this list.
   b) In the middle three.
   c) In the bottom three.

2. Do you consider yourself a 'slave' to fashion, football, TV, music, video games, being in control, etc.?
   a) Not really.
   b) Sometimes.
   c) Definitely.

3. Is it OK to use bad language nowadays?
   a) I try not to. I think it sounds quite ugly.
   b) I'm always careful not to use it in front of grown-ups.
   c) Everyone uses it, so why shouldn't I?

4. It's impossible to express my feelings without using the name of the Lord or other swear words. Do you agree with this statement?

   a) I don't agree. Many people are able to say how they feel without using disrespectful language.
   b) It really depends on the particular situation, so I'm not sure.
   c) I agree with this statement. If you don't swear, people won't realise how angry you really are.

5. Do you think Sunday should be just like any other day of the week?
   a) No. It's the Lord's Day, so I think it's good to take time out for God and make one day different to all the others.
   b) It depends! I go to Mass sometimes, but it can be boring. I like to have a lie-in or go to the shops or watch videos all day too.
   c) Sunday is just like any other day. I don't think we should have to do anything extra on that day.

6. Are there different ways to keep the Sabbath holy?
   a) Yes. You can go to Mass and try to make this day different by being quieter, or taking time for prayer or time with your family.

b) I think it's only about going to Mass.
c) Who cares?

7. Parents and people in charge of us can be a pain in the neck – they won't let us do anything we want. Do you agree?
a) Parents and others who care for us usually have our best interests at heart. It can be hard work, so we need to care for them too.
b) Well, maybe – but sometimes they are right, you know.
c) I agree. I'm fed up being told what to do. What do they know anyway?

8. Living as family means that everyone needs to respect – or 'care for' – everyone else. Is this easy?
a) We learn how to love others when we practise in our families – this is not always easy, but the fourth commandment encourages us to do this.
b) I like it when others care about me, but I don't always care for them in return.
c) I'm not too bothered really – I only look out for number one.

9. Is forgiveness the key?
a) I think forgiveness is the most important thing – there should be no limit to our forgiveness.
b) I'm able to say sorry, but I find it hard to forget if someone hurts me.
c) I never like to say sorry.

10. Do you think that all the violence, anger, murder and nastiness we see on our TV screens affects us?
a) All that violence can lead people to think there's nothing wrong with it, that it does no harm. I think it makes us numb to the pain we can cause others.
b) Some of it is hard to take, but sometimes people just get what they deserve.
c) I don't really notice it anymore.

11. Which of these mottos would you choose?

a) All life is precious!
b) Try to choose life! (Some lives are more valuable than others.)
c) 'Do' others before they 'do' you!

12. Is it ever OK to speak falsely of another?
a) I think we have to try to live the truth at all times – even when we feel tempted to spread a story or rumour.
b) Just make sure it doesn't get back to them!
c) They'll get over it!

13. How would you rate the importance of being faithful to friends?
a) Very important.
b) Quite important.
c) Not very important.

14. Do you think that once you make a commitment to join a club or group, you should make a really good effort to stick with it?
a) It's important to make a good effort.
b) I'm not great at sticking with things, but I try.
c) You can change your mind if you want to at any stage.

15. Some of the other children in the class have the latest mobile phone. Do you think:
a) 'It's really nice for them.'
b) 'I'll pester everyone at home until I get one too.'
c) 'I hope they all break them.'

16. Is it hard to be happy for someone else's success?
a) It's good to celebrate with others.
b) Sometimes.
c) Yes. I'd rather it was me.

17. Is it ever OK to take what is not yours?
a) I don't believe it is.
b) Sometimes – if you're stuck for something.
c) It's OK so long as you don't get caught.

18. We should be generous to those in need – this is part of the seventh commandment too. What do you think?
a) There would be more to go round if one half of the world didn't use so much.
b) I try to give if I have anything left over.
c) As long as I've all I need, I don't care about anyone else.

19. Some people think we are 'stealing' when we use too much of the planet's stores of water, food, trees, air, etc. Do you agree?
a) Yes, I agree. This planet is God's gift, not just for us, but for those coming after us. If we continue to 'steal' all it has, there will be little left to pass on.
b) They have a point, but everyone is at fault, so what can I do?
c) Take all you can get – before someone else gets it.

Mostly As

You are really trying to put into practice in your life, all that the first three commandments ask: 'You only, Lord! You always!' By doing this, you are 'free' to be the truest Christian you can be, right here, right now. Keep it up! You are trying to do the loving thing for others and see things from their viewpoint. 'Love only! Love always!' seems to be your motto in life. You really want to live the commandments!

Mostly Bs

You seem to want the best of all worlds – you need to make some hard choices. Get down off that fence and decide what's worth giving your all to. The first three commandments want you to say with all your heart, 'You only, Lord! You always!' Can you? You genuinely care for others and try to act in a loving way. It can be hard to put others first, but keep working at it!

Mostly Cs

Maybe you need to look again at what's important in your life. Can you begin to find ways to listen to God calling you? Maybe you need to ask yourself before you act: what's the loving thing to do? No one is an island – I can't just care about myself all the time. The commandments call me to care for others too!

At Home   In this lesson we introduce the children to all of the Ten Commandments in the context of God's great love for them.

Pray together:
Let us pray for people who are enslaved in any way.
Let us pray, 'Lord, set them free'. Amen.

Commandments 2

Write out the Ten Commandments on the two stone tablets.

At Home   In this lesson we continue to help the children to reflect on the Ten Commandments. In particular we help
them to become more aware of the commandments in the context of their present-day world.

Pray together:

Our Father who art in heaven, hallowed be thy name.
Thy kingdom come, thy will be done on earth as it is in heaven.
Give us this day our daily bread and forgive us our trespasses
As we forgive those who trespass against us.
And lead us not into temptation but deliver us from evil. Amen.

Advent

Advent is just like a midwife.
Her job is to visit those who
are awaiting the birth of a baby
and help them prepare, now it's due.
She always comes a month beforehand
on a Sunday – the front-door bell rings;
you open it wondering, 'Who on earth's this?'
'It's me – Advent', she sings
cheerfully, joyfully, and enters right in
to the life and soul of the place,
clad all in purple, her evergreen smile
lighting up her rosy pink face.
'So let's have a listen', she says, putting to her ear
that cone-shaped midwife's device,
'…for listening in to the heart of the matter',
she smiles. 'Now, here's my advice;
the Little One who is coming –
according to my reading of the signs –
is well on the way, so if there are things
you need to put right, now's the time!
That's the first thing, and when you've done that,
think about the new baby's name,
make room, in your heart and home – and by the way,
your lives'll never be the same!
But that's just the nature of this new baby;
it will turn your lives inside out,
your world will be turned upside down but don't worry –
that's what this baby's about!'
And so we prepare as Advent advises
and we look forward to the due-date.
'What more can we do now, Advent?' we ask.
She says, 'All we can do now – is wait!'
So that's what we do – wait in joyful hope,
our midwife waits with us too,
and somehow Advent's 'just being there'
gives meaning to the waiting we do.
On Christmas morning she's off out the door,
her midwifeing over and done,
and she leaves in our arms a miracle baby:
Emmanuel! God's newborn Son.

· AN INVITATION

_____

invite you

_____

to join me

as I pray and wait in joyful hope
for the coming of our saviour,
Jesus Christ, at Christmas.

I am Isaiah, the Lord's
prophet.
Listen! Courage! Do not be
afraid!
Look, your God is coming!
He is coming to save you!
Then the eyes of the blind
shall be opened,
the ears of the deaf
unsealed,
the lame shall leap like a
deer
and the tongues of the
dumb shall sing for joy.

ADVENT

Patient People

Advent is like a waiting room
for those who take time to make
an appointment with the Spirit of Christmas,
the real one, that is, not the fake
that's everywhere available, twenty-four seven
and in jingling tills rejoices;
the one you plug-in and it squawks 'Merry Christmas'
in battery-operated voices;
the one whose lights get brighter and brasher
with every year that goes by,
as they try to outdo each other: they'll never
outshine that star in the sky.

Those who have made an appointment
with the true spirit of Christmas know
that waiting rooms are unpopular places
in today's world of get-up-and-go.
What can you do in a waiting room but wait
and wait... till the time is right
and the door to Christmas swings open
and patient people gain insight
to the Christian meaning of Christmas
which sings out in true festive voice,
'Come! Your waiting is over!
Emmanuel! God with us! Rejoice!'

AN INVITATION

I _____

invite you _____

to join me
as I pray and wait in joyful hope
for the coming of our saviour,
Jesus Christ, at Christmas.

Prepare! Prepare!
For One who will come;
His presence among you
Is God's will being done.
Make ready, make straight
A way for God's Son,
Whose presence among you
Is God's kingdom come!

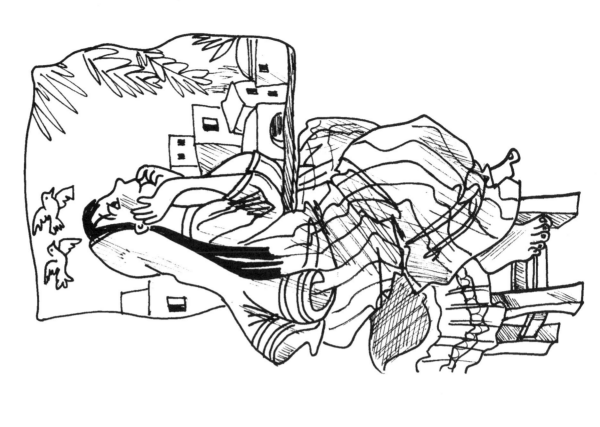

A few Little Moments

The moment the angel appeared
Mary grew worried – and yet
The moment she first heard the news
Was a moment she'd never forget.

The moment she left on her journey
Mary grew worried – and yet
The moment Elizabeth hugged her
Was a moment she'd never forget.

The moment Joseph said, 'Bethlehem'
Mary grew worried – and yet
The moment he said, 'I'll be with you'
Was a moment she'd never forget.

The moment the keeper said, 'No room',
Mary grew worried – and yet
The moment yon little lamb bleated
Was a moment she'd never forget.

The moment her baby first cried
Mary grew worried – and yet
The moment her baby first smiled
She thought, 'This is the best moment yet'.

AN INVITATION

invite you

_____

to join me
as I pray and wait in joyful hope
for the coming of our Saviour,
Jesus Christ, at Christmas.

With all my heart
I praise the Lord,
and I am glad
because of God my Saviour.
God cares for me,
his humble servant.

TERM 2
LESSONS 1-5

Christian Lessons

Write around the outline of the seamless garment: Christian Life, Christian Faith, Christian Community, Christian Morality, Christian Love, Christian Life...
Inside the seamless garment draw pictures from the life of Jesus showing him healing, teaching, telling stories, feeding, praying and breaking bread, with anyone and everyone.

At Home

In these five lessons we help the children to explore the Christian call to grow and develop as it embraces all aspects of life.

Pray together:

Angel sent by God to guide me,
Be my light and walk beside me;
Be my guardian and protect me;
On the paths of life direct me. Amen.

Name the activity in the 'Physical fitness programme'.
Design a 'Lenten fitness programme'.

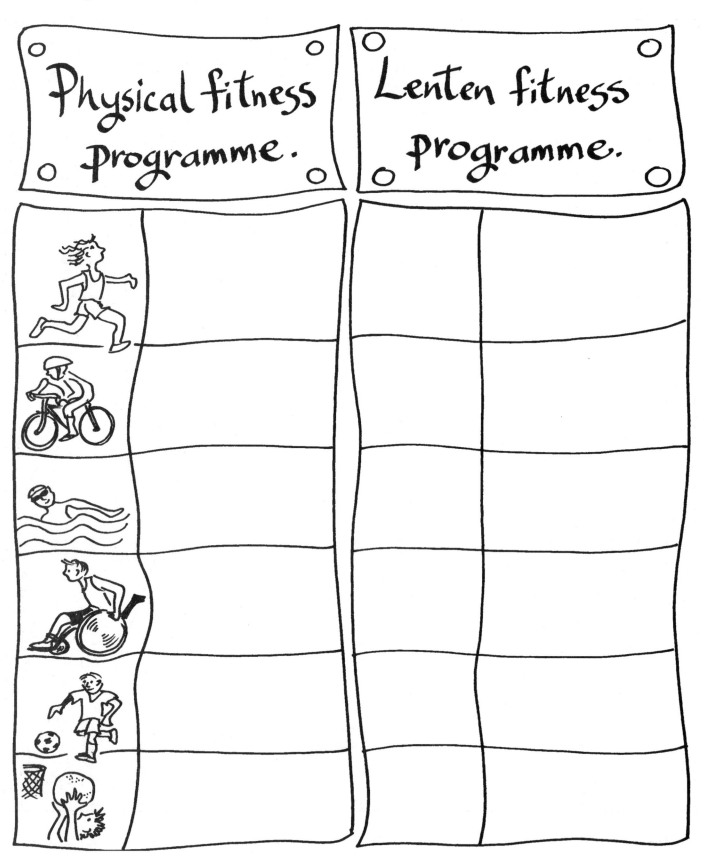

At Home   In this lesson we help the children to enter into the Church season of Lent. This is done by exploring their experience of discipline so that they may grow in fitness for Christian living.

Pray together:
Help us to turn away from sin and be faithful to the gospel.
Help us to turn away from sin, love God and love others. Amen.

Enkindling the Spirit

Look in the wordsearch for words associated with the qualities of fire.

Kindle

flame

spark

destroys

heats

refines

energy

comfort

warms

burns

cheers

melts

At Home

In this lesson we help the children to explore 'fire' as a symbol of the Holy Spirit.

Pray together:

Come, Holy Spirit, fill the hearts of your faithful.
Enkindle in us the fire of your love.
Send forth your spirit and we shall be created,
And you shall renew the face of the earth. Amen.

Spirit Wind

Write the names of the winds in the correct boxes.

At Home

In this lesson we help the children to explore 'wind' as a symbol of the Holy Spirit.

Pray together:

O God, who has taught the hearts of the faithful
by the light of the Holy Spirit,
Grant us in the same spirit to be truly wise,
And ever to rejoice in his consolation,
Through Jesus Christ, our Lord. Amen.

Breath of the Spirit

Write words in the bubbles describing what you can do with your breath.
Colour the bubbles and blend the colours into each other.

At Home

In this lesson we help the children to explore 'breath' as a symbol of the Holy Spirit.

Pray together:

Tar anuas, a Spioraid Naoimh,
Tar anuas, a Spioraid Naoimh,
Tar anuas, a Spioraid Naoimh,
Is líon ár gcroí ded' ghrásta caomh. Áiméan.

Follow this Holy Spirit flow-chart down to one of the gifts at the bottom of the page.

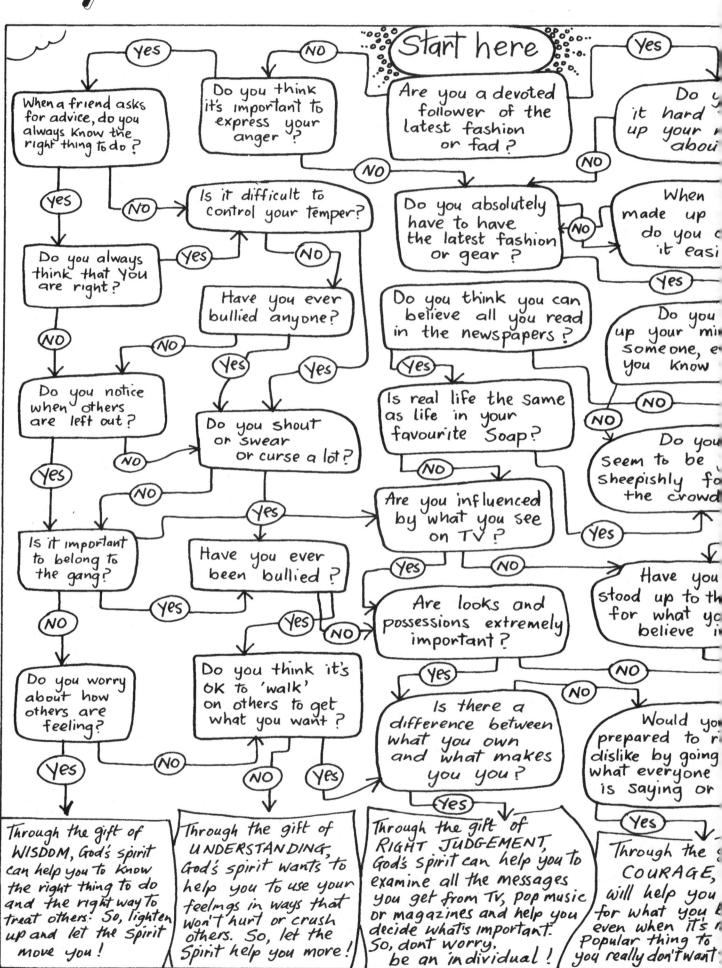

Start here

Are you a devoted follower of the latest fashion or fad?

When a friend asks for advice, do you always know the right thing to do?

Do you think it's important to express your anger?

Do you find it hard to make up your mind about?

Is it difficult to control your temper?

Do you absolutely have to have the latest fashion or gear?

When you've made up do you find it easier?

Do you always think that you are right?

Have you ever bullied anyone?

Do you think you can believe all you read in the newspapers?

Do you make up your mind about someone, even you know?

Do you notice when others are left out?

Do you shout or swear or curse a lot?

Is real life the same as life in your favourite Soap?

Do you seem to be sheepishly following the crowd?

Is it important to belong to the gang?

Have you ever been bullied?

Are you influenced by what you see on TV?

Have you stood up to them for what you believe in?

Do you worry about how others are feeling?

Do you think it's OK to 'walk' on others to get what you want?

Are looks and possessions extremely important?

Is there a difference between what you own and what makes you you?

Would you be prepared to risk dislike by going against what everyone is saying or?

Through the gift of WISDOM, God's spirit can help you to know the right thing to do and the right way to treat others. So, lighten up and let the spirit move you!

Through the gift of UNDERSTANDING, God's spirit wants to help you to use your feelings in ways that won't hurt or crush others. So, let the Spirit help you more!

Through the gift of RIGHT JUDGEMENT, God's spirit can help you to examine all the messages you get from TV, pop music or magazines and help you decide what's important. So, don't worry, be an individual!

Through the gift of COURAGE, will help you for what you even when it's not popular thing to you really don't want

At Home   In this lesson the children are introduced to the following Confirmation elements: gifts of the Spirit, chrism, names and sponsors.

Pray together:
May all those who are anointed
with chrism be inwardly transformed
and come to share in eternal life. Amen.

25

Ceremony of Confirmation (2)

Write the following title on this page: 'The fragrance of Christ fills our lives with…'. Write the fruits of the Spirit on the bottle labels.

At Home
In this lesson we explore the Rite of Confirmation with the children.

Pray together:
On these shoulders the yoke of God's law,
In this head the Spirit of Wonder,
This forehead marked with the Sign of Christ,
The Spirit sound in these ears like thunder. Amen.

Discuss the illustrations on the liturgical year calendar with your partner.
Decorate the calendar, choosing colours to suit the mood of each season.

At Home   In this lesson we give the children the opportunity to nourish their faith in new life by exploring the
Resurrection stories.

Pray together:
Lord, look on your people with kindness
and by these Easter mysteries
bring us to the glory of the Resurrection. Amen.

The Risen Jesus is Present at Mass

Unscramble the words at the bottom of the page and write them under the circles. Draw a picture in each circle illustrating the words.

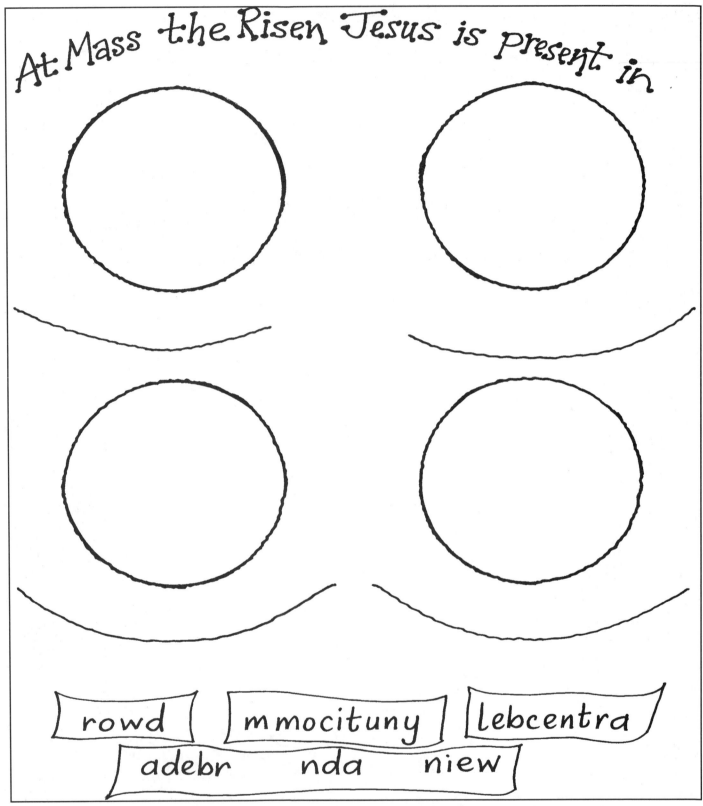

At Mass the Risen Jesus is present in

rowd   mmocituny   lebcentra

adebr   nda   niew

At Home   In this lesson we help the children to come to a deeper understanding of how the Risen Lord Jesus is present at Mass.

Pray together:
Christ, be our light!
Shine in our hearts.
Shine through the darkness.
Christ, be our light!
Shine in your Church gathered today. Amen.

Where do we go from here (1)?

Give **your** best reasons for being a Christian in today's world.

Being a young Christian today is difficult because...

At Home   In this lesson we offer the children (through drama) an opportunity to explore their experience of what it means to be a committed Christian.

Pray together:

God, our Father, I come to say thank you for your love today.
Thank you for my family, and all the friends you give to me.
Guard me in the dark of night, and in the morning send your light. Amen.

ALPHE-O
7

Where do we go from here (2)?

Write the 'Our Father' in Hebrew!
The letters below will help you. (As it is Hebrew, start at the top right-hand corner, and work from right to left.)

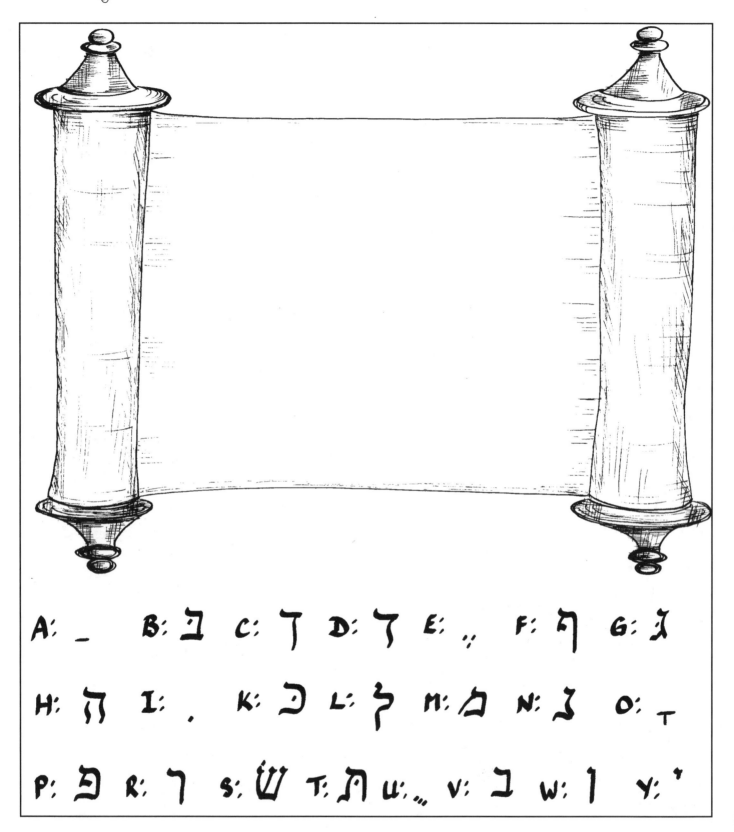

At Home

In this lesson we help the children, through the medium of drama, to make a vital connection with the early Christian community.

Pray together:

O my God, I believe in you
And in all that your Holy Church teaches
Because you have said it
And your word is true. Amen.

Where do we go from here (3)?

Colour in Palestine, Greece (Macedonia) and Rome, and the extent of Roman influence.

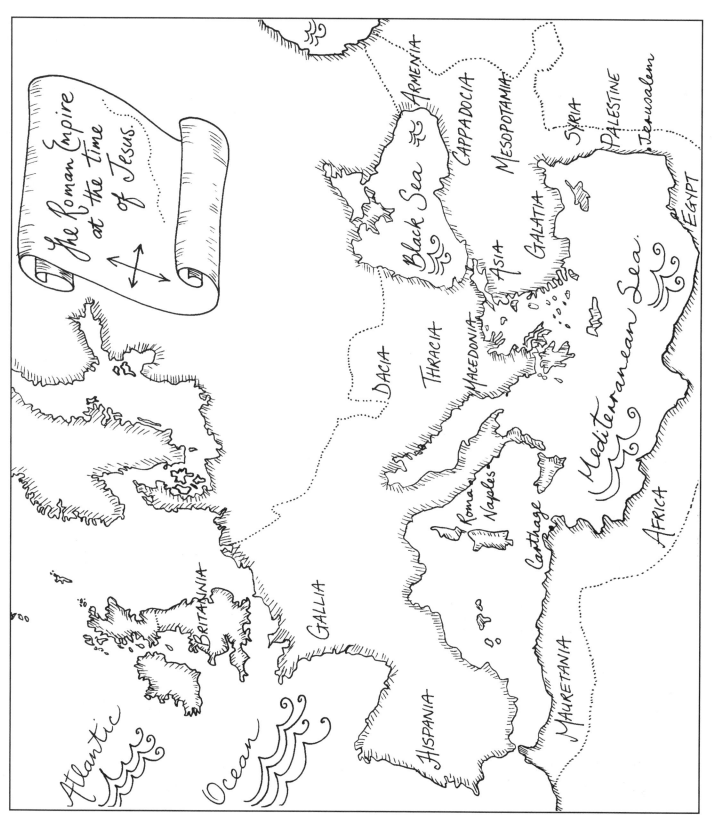

At Home   In this lesson the children are helped, through the medium of drama, to understand the radical nature of Christian forgiveness.

Pray together:

O my God, help me to remember the times
when I didn't live as Jesus asked me to.
Help me to be sorry and to try again. Amen.

Where do we go from here (4)?

Finish the prayers to the saints.

ALIVE-O
7

St Brigid, as I go on from here, help me to...

St Patrick, as I go on from here, help me to...

St Columba, as I go on from here, help me to...

St Gobnait, as I go on from here, help me to...

St Brendan, as I go on from here, help me to...

St Canaire, as I go on from here, help me to...

St Kevin, as I go on from here, help me to...

St Lawrence O'Toole, as I go on from here, help me to...

At Home

In this lesson the children are helped, through the medium of drama, to connect with the early Christian community and its Irish expression.

Pray together:
   Father, all-powerful and ever-living God,
   today we rejoice in the holy men and women
   of every time and place.
   May their prayers bring us your forgiveness and love. Amen.